DAMMIT
SCIENCE
WHERE'S MY
HOVERBOARD?

DAMMIT SCIENCE

WHERE'S MY

HOVERBOARD?

HILARIOUS VISIONS OF THE FUTURE from the Past

EDITED BY
LIAM RYAN

hardie grant books
MELBOURNE · LONDON

CONTENTS

Introduction

I have no idea what is going to happen next, and you probably don't either. None of us really do, and that surprise is half the fun of being human. Fortunately, as you have this book in your hands, the other half of the fun can be found watching others make woefully off-target predictions about what science and technology has in store for us.

When it comes to bad picks about future trends we are in good company. It's not just regular schmoes like me and my brother blowing our Christmas cash on a soon-to-be-redundant MiniDisc stereo. History's finest scientists, politicians and industry leaders get it wrong too. Sometimes these flubs have an optimistic flavour to them, like those futurists of the 1950s whose idea of domestic heaven involved silver onesies and hovering robot maids made of moulded plastic. Meanwhile other misfires, driven by equal parts bravado and delusion, are now saddled with a dramatic irony that time won't shake (I'm looking at you, nuclear-technology-speculation).

Out of context and with the benefit of hindsight many of the quotes from familiar names like Edison, Einstein and the Wright brothers seem to be born of minds as in touch with reality as a gibbon in rollerblades. But the fact is that those generating some off-the-mark predictions were the same brainiacs cooking up most of the correct ones too. They were the geniuses who couldn't help but have ideas and inventions pour out of them. And when you fire out that many new concepts, some are bound to blow up in your face and take the rest of the lab with them.

In this respect the scientist Lord Kelvin (1824–1907) is somewhat of a legend. He got on a real roll and in the space of a few years announced that radio 'had no future', flying machines would never be practical and X-rays would prove to be a 'hoax'. On paper it's an impressive 0-from-3 record, but when you've spent your life driving advances in physics and establishing absolute zero, what's a few dud picks between friends?

Among the promises of moon colonies and kids flying their own helicopters there are also a few amazing instances of people really nailing some far-out visions of the future. For example, in *2001: A Space Odyssey* science fiction writer Arthur C Clarke speculated in great detail about a handheld tablet device that is a dead ringer for today's iPad. But perhaps the most astoundingly accurate predictions come from those forward thinkers of the 1600s who put it out there that humans would eventually make it to the moon, all while living in a time when frigates and witch trials were a pretty big deal. This sort of prescience is startling when you think about how hard it would have been, even 30 years ago, to predict that so much of our work, recreation and social lives would be transplanted to an interconnected web of tubes and boxes in the internet. (Or as Bill Clinton put it in 1996: 'Now even my cat has its own page.')

Some of the pundits who put wacky words on record were of course driven by self-promotion or a desire to mud-sling a rival. As it turns out, mixing PR swagger and retrospection yields some terrific material. While promoting his own brand of direct current electricity, Thomas Edison famously spent much breath slandering alternating current as an invention that was good only for accidentally killing everyone you loved. To prove his point and define the phrase 'taking it up a notch', he even electrocuted an elephant to death – at a public event, no less. While this and other similar spectacles did not hamper the eventual success of the rival current, Edison can surely add 'manufacturing the grimmest family day out in history' to his achievements.

At its core, the best humour is relatable and perhaps that is why the quotes contained here are so funny. We know that in the past we've all made bad predictions about where the future is headed. It's nice to know we share this very human trait with some of the greatest geniuses to ever walk the earth. Or maybe we just like the image of these figurative Wile E Coyotes standing charred in a cloud of smoke, blinking as the debris from another failed scheme pitter-patters to earth around them. Either way, I'm laughing.

Liam Ryan

HOME AND LIFESTYLE

✦ Home fires burning ✦

The home

66 **Many homes in the year 2000 will probably have automated kitchens. The housewife may make out her menu for the coming week, put the necessary foods in storage spaces, and give instructions to her kitchen computer. At the prescribed time mechanical arms would get out the preselected food, cook it, and serve it.** 99

– Glenn T Seaborg, US Atomic Energy Commission, 1967

66 **It resembles a five-foot-two aerosol can on wheels. It is said to be a highly intelligent being, unlike anything seen before. It can speak 250 words and understand 50. It can vacuum the house, serve dinner, babysit and answer the door. 'Well, how do you do?' it might say.** 99

– article in *The New York Times* titled
'Developer Calls it a Robot Butler;
Scoffers Say Screws are Loose', 1977

❝ Researchers in scientific laboratories are trying to develop devices to overcome the pull of gravity ... Factory-Made houses equipped with anti-gravity machinery could be floated above the ground – to catch breezes. ❞

– Arthur Radebaugh, futurist illustrator,
from his series *Closer Than We Think*, 1958–1962

❝ Life in those times will be as nearly a holiday as it is possible to make it. Work will be reduced to a minimum by machinery. ❞

– John Elfreth Watkins, engineer,
looking forward 100 years, 1900

" In time, manufacturing will to a great extent follow the sun. "

– CG Abbot, Smithsonian Institution, predicting that with the development of solar power, deserts would become industrial areas, 1928

" We have gone no further than the halfway stage in the industrial revolution ... This has led a number of inventors to seriously look into the possibility of making a foolproof, 100 per cent robot housewife ... It would have a built-in computer and a memory. It could be trained to know the geography of a house. "

– Meredith Thring, professor at Sheffield University, 1962

"By the year 2000, housewives will probably have a robot maid shaped like a box with one large eye on top, several arms and hands, and long narrow pads on the side for moving about."

– GLENN T SEABORG,
US ATOMIC ENERGY COMMISSION, 1966

❝ Let's push our imaginations ahead and visit the home of the 21st century ... It consists of a cluster of prefabricated modules. This home is as self-sufficient as a space capsule. It recirculates its own water supply and draws all of its electricity from its own fuel cell. ❞

– Walter Cronkite on the TV show *The 21st Century*, 1967

❝ New Coke [will be] the most significant soft drink development in the company's history ... the surest move ever made. ❞

– Roberto Goizueta, Coca-Cola Company chairman on their beverage flop, 1985

Power and lighting

" There is a young madman proposing to light the streets of London - with what do you suppose - with smoke! "

– Sir Walter Scott (1771–1832) on a proposal
to light cities with gas

" Good enough for our transatlantic friends but unworthy of the attention of practical or scientific men. "

– British House of Commons transcript referring to
Edison's light bulb, 1879

" I think I may say without contradiction that when the Paris Exhibition closes, electric light will close with it and no more will be heard of it. "

– Erasmus Wilson,
professor at Oxford University,
1878

66 **There is not the slightest chance that electricity could begin competing in a general way with gas.** **99**

– British House of Commons transcript, 1879

66 **Everyone acquainted with the subject will recognize it as a conspicuous failure.** **99**

– Henry Morton, president of the Stevens Institute of Technology, on Edison's light bulb, 1880

❝ Such startling announcements as these should be depreciated as being unworthy of science and mischievous to its true progress. ❞

– Sir William Siemens reacting to news of
Edison's light bulb, 1880

❝ The electric light is very probably a great invention, and ... let us take it for granted that its future development will be vast. But this, unhappily, cannot be urged as a reason why the pioneer companies should be prosperous. ❞

– *The Economist*, 1882

“ Fooling around with alternating current is just a waste of time. Nobody will use it, ever. ”

“ My personal desire would be to prohibit entirely the use of alternating currents. They are as unnecessary as they are dangerous. ”

– Thomas Edison on the form of electrical current that would soon dominate the market, 1889.

Music

"The phonograph has no commercial value at all. "

– Thomas Edison, 1880s

"Home Taping Is Killing Music. "

– British Phonographic Industry campaign, 1980s

" By next Christmas the iPod will be dead, finished, gone, kaput. "

– Alan Sugar, 2005

Movies

> **" The cinema is little more than a fad. It's canned drama. What audiences really want to see is flesh and blood on the stage. "**
>
> – Charlie Chaplin, 1916

" Adding sound to movies would be like putting lipstick on the *Venus de Milo*. "

– Mary Pickford, silent movie star, 1925

" Speaking movies are impossible. When a century has passed, all thought of our so-called talking pictures will have been abandoned. "

– DW Griffith, director, 1926

" Who the hell wants to hear actors talk? "

– HM Warner, founder of Warner Brothers, 1927

" Talking films are a very interesting invention, but I do not believe they will remain long in fashion. "

– Louis-Jean Lumiere, co-inventor of the film projector, 1929

Books

> **" Printed books will never be the equivalent of handwritten codices, especially since printed books are often deficient in spelling and appearance. "**
>
> – Johannes Trithemius, German scholar, 1492

“Books will soon be obsolete in the public schools. Scholars will be instructed through the eye. It is possible to teach every branch of human knowledge with the motion picture. Our school system will be completely changed inside of ten years. ”

– Thomas Edison, *The New York Dramatic Mirror*, 1913

“Paper will be replaced by material which does not depend upon the slow growth of trees for its production. ”

– *Ladies' Home Journal*, 1931

" The multitude of books is a great evil. "

– MARTIN LUTHER, 1530

TV

" Television won't be able to hold on to any market it captures after the first six months. People will soon get tired of staring at a plywood box every night. "

– Darryl Zanuck, 20th Century Fox movie producer, 1946

" Television? The word is half Greek and half Latin. No good will come of this device. "

– CP Scott (1846–1932),
editor of *The Manchester Guardian*

❝ The average American family hasn't time for television. ❞

– *The New York Times*, 1939

❝ Television won't last. It's a flash in the pan. ❞

– Mary Somerville, broadcaster, 1948

" By 1990, the [television] cable will touch all parts of human life: it will allow students to attend school three days a week, letting them learn at home on the other days over two-way TV. "

– Marvin Cetron and Thomas O'Toole in their book
Encounters with the Future, 1982

" By the end of the decade multi-channel cable television will be commonplace in-home countrywide. TV will be used for armchair shopping, banking, calling emergency services and many other services. "

– Kenneth Baker, British Information
Technology Minister, 1982

66 While theoretically and technically television may be feasible, commercially and financially it is an impossibility, a development of which we need waste little time dreaming. 99

– Lee De Forest, radio pioneer, 1926

66 All a trick. Absolute swindler. What's the good of it? What useful purpose will it serve? 99

– comments from members of Britain's Royal Society after an early demonstration of television, 1926

TRAVEL

✴ Up, up and away! ✴

Automobiles

" The ordinary 'horseless carriage' is at present a luxury for the wealthy; and although its price will probably fall in the future, it will never, of course, come into as common use as the bicycle. "

– *Literary Digest*, 1899

" The horse is here to stay but the automobile is only a novelty – a fad. "

– the Michigan Savings Bank president advising Henry Ford's lawyer not to invest, 1903

"That the automobile has practically reached the limit of its development is suggested by the fact that during the past year no improvements of a radical nature have been introduced. "

– *Scientific American*, 1909

"It is an idle dream to imagine that automobiles will take the place of railways in the long distance movement of passengers. "

– American Road Congress, 1913

66 Within the next few decades,
autos will have folding wings that can
be spread when on a straight stretch
of road so that the machine
can take to the air. 99

– EDDIE RICKENBACKER, WWI PILOT AND WRITER, 1924

❝ There will never be a mass market for motor cars – about 1000 in Europe – because that is the limit on the number of chauffeurs available! ❞

– spokesman for Daimler-Benz, founded in 1928

❝ It does not meet the fundamental technical requirements of a motorcar. ❞

– Lord Rootes' post-war assessment of the soon-to-be enormously popular Volkswagen Beetle, 1946

❝ The Japanese don't make anything the people in the US would want. ❞

– John Foster Dulles, US Secretary of State, 1954

❝ The automobile industry is studying a new kind of specially sensitive car body finish whose colour can be changed at will. An electromagnetic gun would emit rays that would instantly 'repaint' the car in any desired hue or combination – perhaps to harmonize with milady's new fall outfit. ❞

– Arthur Radebaugh, futurist illustrator,
from his series *Closer Than We Think*, 1958–1962

66 **An engineering company plans to test soon its designs for adapting a standard car into an airplane. Henry Smolinski, president of Advanced Vehicle Engineers, says he'll put a Pontiac in the air by the end of the year. His design – a wing, tail and pusher engine assembly attached to the car roof and bottom – will be adapted for a dozen modern cars.** 99

– *Calgary Herald* article, 1970

66 **The Edsel is here to stay.** 99

– Henry Ford on his automobile flop, 1957

" The bus between New York and San Francisco will be equipped with airplanes for trips not on the regular schedule. For diversion, billiard rooms, swimming pool, dancing floor and a bridle path would be available. "

– 'Unique Bus of Future to Duplicate Speed of Railroads',
Modern Mechanix, 1930

" Gasoline engines will soon be rendered obsolete. "

– Thomas Edison, 1910s

" With over fifteen types of foreign cars already on sale here, the Japanese auto industry isn't likely to carve out a big share of the market for itself. "

– *Businessweek, 1968*

Rail

> **" Rail travel at high speed is not possible, because passengers, unable to breathe, would die of asphyxia. "**
>
> – Dr Dionysius Lardner, science writer, 1823

" **What can be more palpably absurd than the prospect held out of locomotives traveling twice as fast as stagecoaches?** "

– *The Quarterly Review*, 1825

" **Dear Mr President. The canal system of this country is being threatened by a new form of transportation known as 'railroads' ... carriages are pulled at the enormous speed of 15 miles per hour by 'engines' which, in addition to endangering life and limb of passengers, roar and snort their way through the countryside, setting fire to crops, scaring the livestock and frightening women and children. The Almighty certainly never intended that people should travel at such breakneck speed.** "

– Martin Van Buren, Governor of New York, 1829

❝ No one will pay good money to get from Berlin to Potsdam in one hour when he can ride his horse there in one day for free. ❞

– King William I of Prussia passes comment
on rail travel, 1864

❝ It may, however, be safe to assume that it will hardly be possible to apply electricity to haul great passenger trains. ❞

– George H Daniels, railway executive, 1900

Flight

66 It is apparent to me that the possibilities of the aeroplane, which two or three years ago were thought to hold the solution to the [flying machine] problem, have been exhausted, and that we must turn elsewhere. 99

– Thomas Edison, 1895

66 I have not the smallest molecule of faith in aerial navigation other than ballooning. 99

– Lord Kelvin, physicist and engineer, 1890

**❝ Heavier-than-air flying machines
are impossible. ❞**

– Lord Kelvin, physicist and engineer, 1899

**❝ ... no possible combination of known substances,
known forms of machinery, and known forms
of force can be united in a practicable machine
by which men shall fly for long distances
through the air. ❞**

– Simon Newcomb,
astronomer and mathematician, 1900s

" Flight by machines heavier than air is unpractical and insignificant, if not utterly impossible. "

– Simon Newcomb,
astronomer and mathematician, 1902

" All attempts at artificial aviation are not only dangerous to life but doomed to failure from an engineering standpoint. "

– editor of *The Times* in London, 1905

" Man will not fly for 50 years. "

– Wilbur Wright in 1901,
two years before he and
his brother Orville took flight

" I confess that in 1901 I said to my brother Orville
that man would not fly for 50 years. Two years
later we ourselves made flights. This demonstration
of my impotence as a prophet gave me such a
shock that ever since I have distrusted myself
and avoided all predictions. "

– Wilbur Wright, 1908

" No flying machine will ever fly from
New York to Paris. "

– Orville Wright, 1908

66 **'Let's all fly like the birdies do.' That might well become a slogan – with the development of a kind of flying machine which keeps aloft by flapping its wings.** 99

– Arthur Radebaugh, futurist illustrator, from his series
Closer Than We Think, 1958–1962

66 **No balloon and no aeroplane will ever be practically successful.** 99

– Lord Kelvin, physicist and engineer, 1902

" There will never be a bigger plane built. "

– Boeing engineer referring to the
247 twin-engine plane
that would hold 10 people, 1932

" Automobiles will start to decline almost as soon as the last shot is fired in World War II. The name of Igor Sikorsky will be as well known as Henry Ford's, for his helicopter will all but replace the horseless carriage as the new means of popular transportation. Instead of a car in every garage, there will be a helicopter ... These 'copters' will be so safe and will cost so little to produce that small models will be made for teenage youngsters. These tiny copters, when school lets out, will fill the sky as the bicycles of our youth filled the prewar roads. "

– Harry Bruno, aviation industry publicist, 1943

" Very interesting, Whittle my boy,
but it will never work. "

– Cambridge aeronautics professor responding to jet
pioneer Frank Whittle's plans for a jet engine, 1930

" ... a practical, working rocket belt, torn from the pages of science fiction, has made a reality of mankind's age-old dream of flying with the birds. "

– ASSOCIATED PRESS ARTICLE JUMPING THE GUN FOLLOWING AN EARLY TRIAL OF A JETPACK, 1961

Boats

" **What, Sir, would you make a ship sail against the wind and currents by lighting a bonfire under her deck? I pray you, excuse me, I have not the time to listen to such nonsense.** "

– Napoleon Bonaparte's reaction to news of Robert Fulton's steamboat, early 1803

" Men might as well project a voyage to the Moon as attempt to employ steam navigation against the stormy North Atlantic Ocean. "

– Dr Dionysus Lardner,
Professor of Natural Philosophy and Astronomy
at University College, London, 1800s

" I must confess that my imagination refuses to see any sort of submarine doing anything but suffocating its crew and floundering at sea. "

– HG Wells, 1901

COMMUNI-CATIONS

✴ Greetings, earthlings! ✴

Telegraph, telephone and fax

" I watched his countenance closely, to see if he was not deranged ... and I was assured by other senators after he left the room that they had no confidence in it. "

– US Senator Oliver Smith after a demonstration of Morse's telegraph, 1842

" It's a great invention but who would want to use it anyway? "

– attributed to US President Rutherford B Hayes, following a demonstration of Alexander Bell's telephone, 1876

" **This 'telephone' has too many shortcomings to be seriously considered as a means of communication. The device is inherently of no value to us.** "

– Western Union
internal memo, 1876

❝ The Americans have need of the telephone, but we do not. We have plenty of messenger boys. ❞

– William Preece, British Post Office chief engineer, 1878

❝ Translating machines will soon take their place beside gramophone records and colour reproduction in the first rank of modern techniques for the spread of culture and science. ❞

– Emile Delavenay, 1958

❝ To call Sweden from Washington in the year 2001 you might pick up your all-language videophone, speak the number – dialing, including push-buttons, would be obsolete – and when the circuit is established, converse in your own language. ❞

– Daniel J Fink, US Defence Department researcher, 1966

❝ The possibility of an inexpensive video-telephone in every home was advanced Wednesday as the Bell System reported results of the first commercial test of a new lightweight communications technology ... the test is so successful that the Bell System is developing a full-scale light wave communications system for installation in 1980. ❞

– Reuters article, 1978

" Transmission of documents via telephone wires is possible in principle, but the apparatus required is so expensive that it will never become a practical proposition. "

– Dennis Gabor,
physicist, 1962

Radio

" Well-informed people know it is impossible to transmit the voice over wires, and that were it possible to do so, the thing would be of no practical value. "

– *Boston Post* editorial, 1865

" Don't waste time on foolish ideas. Radio has no future. "

– Lord Kelvin, physicist and engineer, 1899

❝ The wireless music box has no imaginable commercial value. Who would pay for a message sent to nobody in particular? ❞

– INVESTOR RESPONDING TO RCA EXECUTIVE DAVID SARNOFF'S
REQUEST FOR SUPPORT FOR THE RADIO, 1920S

❝ Lee De Forest has said in many newspapers and over his signature that it would be possible to transmit the human voice across the Atlantic before many years. Based on these absurd and deliberately misleading statements, the misguided public has been persuaded to purchase stock in his company. ❞

– US District Attorney indicting radio pioneer Lee De Forest for fraud, 1913

❝ The radio craze will die out in time. ❞

– Thomas Edison, 1922

Computers and the internet

66 It would appear that we have reached the limits of what it is possible to achieve with computer technology. Although one should be careful with such statements as they tend to sound pretty silly in five years. 99

– John von Neumann, computer scientist, 1949

66 ... computers in the future may have only 1000 vacuum tubes and weigh only 1.5 tons. 99

– *Popular Mechanics*, 1949

" I have traveled the length and breadth of this country and talked with the best people, and I can assure you that data processing is a fad that won't last out the year. "

– Prentice Hall editor in charge of business books, 1957

" The world potential market for copying machines is 5000 at most. "

– IBM statement after turning down an offer from the company that would become Xerox, 1959

" **A computer for the housewife [would] make up your grocery lists, plan your menus, remind you of appointments, balance your checkbook, pay your household bills, easily figure out your income tax and give you the best tax break while at it ... you would type your orders, questions etc., the machine would put everything you said in storage and then it would type out the answers to your questions, the reminders, lists and notes as you need them.** "

– George L Haller, General Electric vice president for Advanced Technology Services, 1964

66 **[By 1985], machines will be capable of doing any work Man can do.** 99

– Herbert A Simon, a founder in the field of artificial intelligence, 1965

66 **By 2000, the machines will be producing so much that everyone in the US will, in effect, be independently wealthy.** 99

– *Time*, 1966

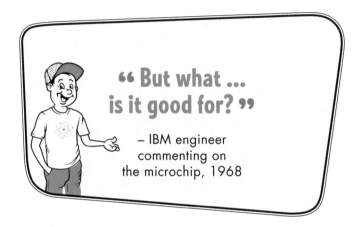

**" But what ...
is it good for? "**

– IBM engineer
commenting on
the microchip, 1968

" Remote shopping, while entirely feasible, will flop because women like to get out of the house, like to handle merchandise, like to be able to change their minds. "

– Time, 1966

" The nation's first home computer service, which brought customers computer services by telephone, is going out of business after six months because people don't trust computers. "

– Williamson Daily News, 1973

" So we went to Atari and said, 'Hey, we've got this amazing thing, even built with some of your parts, and what do you think about funding us? Or we'll give it to you. We just want to do it. Pay our salary, we'll come work for you.' And they said, 'No.' So then we went to Hewlett Packard, and they said, 'Hey, we don't need you. You haven't got through college yet. "

– Steve Jobs on attempts to generate interest in his personal computer prototype in the 1970s

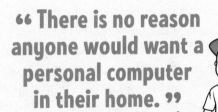

"There is no reason anyone would want a personal computer in their home."

– Ken Olson,
Digital Equipment founder, 1977

**" When it comes to information retrieval
I doubt if there really is the market out there that
home computer manufacturers think there is.
The American wife has a memory far superior
to any computer, at least she does in my house. "**

– Art Buchwald, humourist 1977

**" $100 million is way too much to
pay for Microsoft. "**

– IBM, 1982

" We will never make a 32-bit operating system. "

– Bill Gates, 1983

" This antitrust thing will blow over. "

– Bill Gates, 1995

**" Y2K is a crisis without precedent
in human history. "**

– Edmund DeJesus, editor of *Byte Magazine*, 1998

66 I predict the internet ... will soon go spectacularly supernova and in 1996 catastrophically collapse. 99

– ROBERT METCALFE, ETHERNET INVENTOR, 1995

" The truth is no online database will replace your daily newspaper, no CD-ROM can take the place of a competent teacher and no computer network will change the way government works. "

– Clifford Stoll, author, 1995

" By the turn of the century, we will live in a paperless society. "

– Roger Smith, General Motors chairman, 1986

66 **By 2005 or so, it will become clear that the internet's impact on the economy has been no greater than the fax machine's.** 99

– Paul Krugman, economist, 1998

66 **These Google guys, they want to be billionaires and rock stars and go to conferences and all that. Let us see if they still want to run the business in two to three years.** 99

– Bill Gates, 2003

" There's just not that many videos I want to watch "

– YouTube co-founder Steve Chen when the site featured only a few dozen videos, 2005

" I give [Apple] two years before they're turning out the lights on a very painful and expensive mistake. "

– president of Channel Marketing David Goldstein, claiming the Apple Stores could never succeed, *BusinessWeek*, 2001

" There's no chance that the iPhone is going to get any significant market share. No chance. "

– Steve Ballmer,
Microsoft CEO, 2007

SPACE, WAR AND THE ATOM

AND THE ATOM

✴ We come in peace ✴

Space

" A rocket will never be able to leave the Earth's atmosphere. "

– The New York Times, 1920

" Professor Goddard does not know the relation between action and reaction and the need to have something better than a vacuum against which to react. He seems to lack the basic knowledge ladled out daily in high schools. "

– The New York Times on Robert Goddard's pioneering rocket work, 1921

66 There is no hope for the fanciful idea of reaching the moon, because of the insurmountable barriers to escaping the earth's gravity. **99**

– FR MOULTON, ASTRONOMER, 1932

" To place a man in a multi-stage rocket and project him into the controlling gravitational field of the moon where the passengers can make scientific observations, perhaps land alive, and then return to earth – all that constitutes a wild dream worthy of Jules Verne. I am bold enough to say that such a man-made voyage will never occur regardless of all future advances. "

– Lee De Forest,
radio pioneer, 1957

" Space travel is utter bilge. "

– Richard Woolley,
Astronomer Royal of the UK, 1956

" Space travel is bunk. "

– Harold Spencer Jones,
Astronomer Royal of the UK, 1957

66 Man on earth can no more get rid of these demonic 'heavens' than man can by airplane or rockets or other means get up above the air envelope which is about our earthly globe and in which man breathes. 99

– Watchtower Bible and Tract Society, 1943

66 The foolish idea of shooting at the moon is an example of the absurd length to which vicious specialization will carry scientists working in thought-tight compartments. 99

– AW Bickerton, physicist, 1926

" There is practically no chance communications space satellites will be used to provide better telephone, telegraph, television, or radio service inside the United States. "

– T Craven,
US Federal Communications
Commissioner, 1961

" Before man reaches the moon, your mail will be delivered within hours from New York to Australia by guided missiles. We stand on the threshold of rocket mail. "

– Arthur Summerfield, US Postmaster General, 1959

" A number of man-made moons will be circling around the earth ... Journeys through space in rocket ships will be an established form of transportation, with regularly scheduled trips to the various planets. "

– Henry C Nicholas in the article 'Cheer Up! World Will Be Wonderful Fifty Years From Now!', 1952

"With the first moon colonies predicted for the 70s, preliminary work is moving ahead on the types of shelter that will be required to maintain men on the moon."

– Arnold Barach in his book *1975 and the Changes to Come*, 1962

"The lunar outpost is required to develop and protect potential United States interests on the moon."

– a 1957 US Military report for Project Horizon calling for 12 troops and missiles to be stationed on the moon by 1966

❝ [By 2001] an economical manned transportation system to the near planets - Mars and Venus - is likely to be either in service or in active development. ❞

– Eugene Konecci, the President's Space Council, 1966

❝ Further investigation and experimentation have confirmed the findings of Isaac Newton in the 17th century and it is now definitely established that a rocket can function in a vacuum as well as in an atmosphere. The *Times* regrets the error. ❞

– a retraction of a 1920 article, printed by
The New York Times during Apollo 11's successful
mission to the moon, 1969

66 **A partnership between government and industry could establish a colony on the moon within 20 years.** 99

– Michael Duke, NASA, 1986

66 **The Earth Spaceport is envisioned as a permanent center optimized to support transportation operations ... The capabilities of Earth Spaceport would be expected to grow with time, expanding ... to support the Bridge between Worlds before 2010.** 99

– National Commission on Space in its report 'Pioneering the Space Frontier: Our Next 50 Years in Space', 1986

Nuclear power and the A-bomb

❝ There is no likelihood that man can ever tap the power of the atom. The glib supposition of utilizing atomic energy when our coal has run out is a completely unscientific utopian dream, a childish bug-a-boo. ❞

– Robert Millikan, Nobel Prize-winning physicist, 1928

❝ There is not the slightest indication that nuclear energy will ever be obtainable. It would mean that the atom would have to be shattered at will. ❞

– Albert Einstein, 1932

" The energy produced by the breaking down of the atom is a very poor kind of thing. Anyone who expects a source of power from the transformation of these atoms is talking moonshine. "

– Ernest Rutherford,
chemist and physicist, 1933

" Atomic energy might be as good as our present-day explosives, but it is unlikely to produce anything very much more dangerous. "

– Winston Churchill, 1939

" The bomb will never go off. I speak as an expert in explosives. "

– William Leahy, US Admiral, 1944

" Our children will enjoy in their homes electrical energy too cheap to meter ... "

– Lewis Strauss, chairman of the US Atomic Energy Commission, 1954

" There is little doubt that the most significant event affecting energy is the advent of nuclear power ... a few decades hence, energy may be free – just like the unmetered air ... "

– John von Neumann, scientist and member of the Atomic Energy Commission, 1955

66 *Nuclear-powered vacuum cleaners will probably be a reality in 10 years.* 99

– ALEX LEWYT, PRESIDENT OF VACUUM CLEANER COMPANY
LEWYT CORP, 1955

" The basic questions of design, material and shielding, in combining a nuclear reactor with a home boiler and cooling unit, no longer are problems ... The system would heat and cool a home, provide unlimited household hot water, and melt the snow from sidewalks and driveways. All that could be done for six years on a single charge of fissionable material costing about $300. "

– Robert Ferry, US Institute of Boiler and Radiator Manufacturers, 1955

" All the waste in a year from a nuclear power plant can be stored under a desk. "

– Ronald Reagan, 1980

War

" I also lay aside all ideas of any new works or engines of war, the invention of which long-ago reached its limit, and in which I see no hope for further improvement ... "

– Sextus Julius Frontinus, 84AD

" No, it will make war impossible. "

– machine gun inventor Hiram Maxim responding to the question 'Will this gun not make war more terrible?', 1893

" ... transport by railroad car would result in the emasculation of our troops and would deprive them of the option of the great marches which have played such an important role in the triumph of our armies. "

– Dominique Francois Arago (1786–1853)

" The invention of aircraft will make war impossible in the future. "

– George Gissing, early 1900s

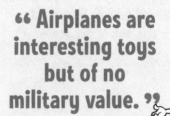

" Airplanes are interesting toys but of no military value. "

– Marshal Ferdinand Foch, 1911

66 It must be accepted as a principle that the rifle, effective as it is, cannot replace the effect produced by the speed of the horse, the magnetism of the charge and the terror of cold steel. 99

– British Cavalry training manual, 1907

66 The coming of the wireless era will make war impossible, because it will make war ridiculous. 99

– Guglielmo Marconi, radio pioneer, 1912

" The machine gun is a much overrated weapon; two per battalion is more than sufficient. "

– General Douglas Haig, 1915

" Caterpillar landships are idiotic and useless. Nobody has asked for them and nobody wants them. Those officers and men are wasting their time and are not pulling their proper weight in the war. "

– Fourth Lord of the British Admiralty, 1915

❝The idea that cavalry will be replaced by these iron coaches is absurd. It is little short of treasonous. ❞

– Douglas Haig's personal assistant at a tank demonstration, 1916

" **... too far-fetched to be considered.** "

– *Scientific American* editor referring to a rocket-accelerated aeroplane bomb, 1940

❝ Had the European governments foreseen the part which the aeroplane was to play they would never have entered upon the war. ❞

– Orville Wright, on how airplanes
could promote peace, 1917

❝ The Americans are good about making fancy cars and refrigerators, but that doesn't mean they are any good at making aircraft. They are bluffing. They are excellent at bluffing. ❞

– Hermann Goering, 1942

BACK TO SCHOOL

Physics, maths, chemistry, astronomy, geology, health and biology

Planet Earth and biology

❝ Animals, which move, have limbs and muscles; the earth has no limbs and muscles, hence it does not move. ❞

– Scipio Chiaramonti, University of Pisa, 1633

❝ My recent studies have made me more adverse than ever to the new scientific doctrines which are flourishing now in England. This sensational zeal reminds me of what I experienced as a young man in Germany ... I trust to outlive this mania also. ❞

– Louis Agassiz, professor of geology and zoology at Harvard University, criticising Darwin's theories, 1867

" I see no good reasons why the views given in this volume should shock the religious sensibilities of anyone. "

– Charles Darwin,
in *The Origin of Species*,
1859

"Strawberries as large as apples will be eaten by our great-great-grandchildren for their Christmas dinners."

– *Ladies' Home Journal* speculating on developments 100 years in the future, 1900

"... even Americans will probably be subjected to water rationing by 1974 and food rationing by the end of the decade."

– Paul Ehrlich, biologist, 1970

" **The world will be about ... 11 degrees colder in the year 2000. This is about twice what it would take to put us into an ice age.** "

– Kenneth Watt, ecologist, 1970

" **By 1985, air pollution will have reduced the amount of sunlight reaching earth by one half ...** "

– *Life* magazine, 1970

❝ The world's climate is changing. Of that scientists are firmly convinced ... Sooner or later, a major cooling of the climate is widely considered inevitable. ❞

– *The New York Times*, 1975

❝ The dangers of carbon dioxide? Tell that to a plant, how dangerous carbon dioxide is. ❞

– US Presidential hopeful Rick Santorum supporting his claim that climate change is a hoax, 2012

Health

" The seat of the soul and the control of voluntary movement - in fact of nervous functions in general - are to be sought in the heart. The brain is an organ of minor importance, perhaps necessary to cool the blood. "

– Aristotle, (384–322BC)

" Stated simply, you may have a positive chance of surviving clinical death. "

– a brochure promoting cryogenic freezing of humans from the Cryonics Society of California, 1980

" Your cigarettes will never become popular. "

– FG Alton, cigar maker, turning down John Player, 1870

" If excessive smoking actually plays a role in the production of lung cancer, it seems to be a minor one. "

– WC Hueper, National Cancer Institute, 1954

" Recent scientific investigations have proved that dancing must bear a part of the responsibility for the increase of tuberculosis among young people. Addiction to the terpsichorean diversion usually results in loss of sleep, which cannot be made up adequately on other nights. Insufficient rest and sleep lowers bodily resistance and gives the tuberculosis germs an easy conquest. Daylight saving also has a hand in inflicting tuberculosis on young people, since it shortens the time permitted for sleeping. "

– *Modern Mechanics and Inventions*, 1932

" X-rays will prove to be a hoax. "

– Lord Kelvin, physicist and engineer, 1899

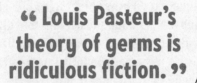

" Louis Pasteur's theory of germs is ridiculous fiction. "

– Pierre Pachet,
professor of Physiology
at Toulouse, 1872

" The abdomen, the chest, and the brain will forever be shut from the intrusion of the wise and humane surgeon. "

– John Erichsen, British surgeon, 1873

" The abolishment of pain in surgery is a chimera. It is absurd to go on seeking it ... knife and pain are two words in surgery that must forever be associated in the consciousness of the patient. "

– Alfred Velpeau, French surgeon, 1839

> **Modern alchemists may create food pills that would contain everything necessary for life – a feat that would render man forever independent of natural resources for his nourishment, and banish fear of crop failure and famine.**

– POPULAR SCIENCE MONTHLY, 1936

❝ That virus is a pussycat. ❞

– Peter Duesberg, molecular-biology professor at University
of California, Berkeley, in reference to HIV, 1988

❝ We can close the books on infectious diseases. ❞

– William Stewart,
US Surgeon General, 1969

Astronomy

" People give ear to an upstart astrologer who strove to show that the earth revolves, not the heavens or the firmament, the Sun and the Moon ... This fool wishes to reverse the entire science of astronomy ... "

– Martin Luther (1483–1546) criticising Copernicus

" Mathematics is inadequate to describe the universe, since mathematics is an abstraction from natural phenomena. Also, mathematics may predict things which don't exist, or are impossible in nature. "

– Lodovico delle Colombe (1565–1616) criticising Galileo

" The view that the Earth is not the center of the universe and even has a daily rotation is philosophically false, and at least an erroneous belief. "

– Roman Catholic Church edict, 1616

" Comets are not heavenly bodies, but originate in the Earth's atmosphere below the Moon. "

– Father Augustin de Angelis,
Clementine College, 1673

" I would sooner believe that two Yankee professors lied, than that stones fell from the sky. "

– US President Thomas Jefferson, on hearing
reports of meteorites, 1790s

" We are probably nearing the limit of all we can know about astronomy. "

– Simon Newcomb, astronomer, 1888

Chemistry, physics and maths

" **The good Christian should beware of mathematicians, and all those who make empty prophecies. The danger already exists that the mathematicians have made a covenant with the devil to darken the spirit and confine man in the bonds of Hell.** "

– Saint Augustine (354–430AD)

" The more important fundamental laws and facts of physical science have all been discovered, and these are now so firmly established that the possibility of their ever being supplanted in consequence of new discoveries is exceedingly remote ... Our future discoveries must be looked for in the sixth place of decimals. "

– Albert A Michelson, physicist, 1903

❝ There is nothing new to be discovered in physics now. All that remains is more and more precise measurement. ❞

– Lord Kelvin, physicist and engineer, 1900

❝ I am tired of all this thing called science here. We have spent millions in that sort of thing for the last few years, and it is time it should be stopped. ❞

– Simon Cameron, US Senator, 1901

66 *It doesn't matter what he does, he will never amount to anything.* 99

– ALBERT EINSTEIN'S TEACHER TO HIS FATHER, 1895

" I can accept the theory of relativity as little as I can accept the existence of atoms and other such dogma. "

– Ernst Mach, 1910s

" [By 1940] the relativity theory will be considered a joke. "

– George Francis Gillette, 1929

THE BRIGHT IDEA...

✴ Those who got it right ✴

" The Art of Flying is but newly invented, 'twill improve by degrees, and in time grow perfect; then we may fly as far as the Moon. "

– Bernard le Bovier de Fontenelle, 1686.

" I have discovered that a screw-shaped device such as this, if it is well made from starched linen, will rise in the air if turned quickly. "

– Leonardo da Vinci,
describing his helical air screw, 1480

" I can well appreciate, Holy Father, that as soon as certain people realise that in these books which I have written about the revolutions of the spheres of the universe, I attribute certain motions to the globe of the Earth, they will at once clamour for me to be hooted off the stage with such an opinion. "

– Nicolaus Copernicus, 1543

" Ships and sails proper for the heavenly air should be fashioned. Then there will also be people, who do not shrink from the dreary vastness of space. "

– Johannes Kepler, letter to Galileo, 1609

135

" In space there are countless constellations, suns and planets; we see only the suns because they give light; the planets remain invisible, for they are small and dark. There are also numberless earths circling around their suns, no worse and no less than this globe of ours. **"**

– Giordano Bruno, astronomer who was later burnt at the stake for heresy, *De l'Infinito, Universo, e Mondi*, 1584

❝ Flying. Whatever any other organism has been able to do man should surely be able to do also, though he may go a different way about it. ❞

– Samuel Butler, novelist (1835–1902)

❝ I suppose we shall soon travel by air-vessels; make air instead of sea voyages; and at length find our way to the moon, in spite of the want of atmosphere. ❞

– Lord Byron, 1882

❝ I have not failed. I've just found 10,000 ways that won't work. ❞

– Thomas Edison (1847–1931)

❝ Wireless telephone and telegraph circuits will span the world. A husband in the middle of the Atlantic will be able to converse with his wife sitting in her boudoir in Chicago. We will be able to telephone to China quite as readily as we now talk from New York to Brooklyn. ❞

– John Elfreth Watkins, engineer, 1900

" Photographs will be telegraphed from any distance. If there be a battle in China a hundred years hence, snapshots of its most striking events will be published in the newspapers an hour later ... photographs will reproduce all of nature's colours. "

– John Elfreth Watkins, engineer, 1900

❝ The improved 'limitless-distance' telephone was presently introduced, and the daily doings of the globe made visible to everybody, and audibly discussable too, by witnesses separated by any number of leagues. ❞

– Mark Twain describes a world with a 'telectroscope' network not unlike the internet, 1904

❝ If I had asked people what they wanted, they would have said faster horses. ❞

– Henry Ford (1863–1947)

66 **Trying to predict the future is like trying to drive down a country road at night with no lights while looking out the back window.** 99

– Peter Drucker, business thinker and author (1909–2005)

66 **Dr EO Hulburt, physicist of the naval research laboratory, Washington, has found conclusive mathematical evidence that the earth's temperature is being warmed by the increased amount of carbon dioxide present in the air. Smoke stacks emit huge volumes of this gas, which is also found in the breath and waste products of humans and animals.** 99

– *Modern Mechanics and Inventions*, 1932

66 Television in the home is now technically feasible. The difficulties confronting this difficult and complicated art can only be solved from operating experience, actually serving the public in their homes. 99

– David Sarnoff, RCA, 1938

66 ... he would plug in his foolscap-size newspad into the ship's information circuit and scan the latest reports from Earth. One by one he would conjure up the world's major electronic papers ... he would hold the front page while he quickly searched the headlines and noted the items that interested him. Each had its own two-digit reference; when he punched that, the postage-stamp-size rectangle would expand until it neatly filled the screen and he could read it with comfort. When he had finished, he would flash back to the complete page and select a new subject for detailed examination ... 99

– Arthur C Clarke in *2001: A Space Odyssey*, accurately describing an almost-iPad, 1968

" *Big Brother is watching you.* "

– GEORGE ORWELL FROM HIS NOVEL NINETEEN EIGHTY-FOUR,
DESCRIBING NETWORKS OF VIDEO SURVEILLANCE, 1949

" Each new machine or technique, in a sense, changes all existing machines and techniques, by permitting us to put them together into new combinations. The number of possible combinations rises exponentially as the number of new machines or techniques rises arithmetically. Indeed, each new combination may, itself, be regarded as a new super-machine. "

– Alvin Toffler, futurist, 1970

" The best way to predict the future is to invent it. "

– Alan Kay, computer scientist, 1971

66 If we had a reliable way to label our toys good and bad, it would be easy to regulate technology wisely. But we can rarely see far enough to know which road leads to damnation. 99

– Freeman Dyson, physicist and mathematician, 1979

66 Since we have no choice but to be swept along by [this] vast technological surge, we might as well learn to surf. 99

– Michael Soule, biologist and conservationist, 1989

" When I took office, only high energy physicists had ever heard of what is called the World Wide Web ... Now even my cat has its own page. "

– Bill Clinton, 1996

" The Internet is becoming the town square for the global village of tomorrow. "

– Bill Gates, 2003

" The so-called generation gap is a consequence of the rate of social and technological change. Even within a human lifetime, the change is so great that many people are alienated from their own society. Margaret Mead had described older people as involuntary immigrants from the past to the present. "

— Carl Sagan, astronomer, 1975

" We'll communicate with it through a variety of devices, including some that look like television sets, some like today's PCs; some will look like telephones, and some will be the size and something like the shape of a wallet. And at the heart of each will be a powerful computer, invisibly connected to millions of others. "

– Bill Gates, 1995

THE END

Published in 2013 by Hardie Grant Books

Hardie Grant Books (Australia)
Ground Floor, Building 1
658 Church Street
Richmond, Victoria 3121
www.hardiegrant.com.au

Hardie Grant Books (UK)
Dudley House, North Suite
34–35 Southampton Street
London WC2E 7HF
www.hardiegrant.co.uk

Copyright © Hardie Grant Books 2013
Dammit Science, Where's My Hoverboard?

ISBN 9781-74270-655-9
Publishing director: Paul McNally
Project editor: Hannah Koelmeyer
Design manager: Heather Menzies
Cover and text designer: Luke Lucas
Production manager: Todd Rechner

Colour reproduction by Splitting Image Colour Studio
Printed and bound in China by 1010 Printing
International Limited

Every effort has been made to correctly attribute the quotes
within this book. Any errors will be incorporated in future
reprints or editions of this book.